MAKING THE GRADE

EASY POPULAR PIECES FOR YOUNG ALTO SAXOPHONISTS. SELECTED AND ARRA

Published by
Chester Music
8/9 Frith Street, London W1D 3JB, England.

Exclusive Distributors:
Music Sales Limited
Distribution Centre, Newmarket Road, Bury St. Edmunds, Suffolk IP33 3YB, England.
Music Sales Pty Limited
120 Rothschild Avenue, Rosebery, NSW 2018, Australia.

Music arranged and processed by Jerry Lanning.
Edited by Heather Ramage.
Printed in the United Kingdom by Caligraving Limited, Thetford, Norfolk.

CD recorded, mixed and mastered by Jonas Persson.
Saxophone by John Whelan.

www.musicsales.com

This publication is not authorised for sale in the
United States of America and/or Canada.

Chester Music
part of The Music Sales Group
London/New York/Paris/Sydney/Copenhagen/Berlin/Madrid/Tokyo

INTRODUCTION

This collection of 21 popular tunes has been carefully arranged and graded to provide attractive teaching repertoire for young alto saxophonists. The familiarity of the material will stimulate pupils' enthusiasm and encourage their practice.

The technical demands of the solo part increase progressively up to the standard of Associated Board Grade 1. The piano accompaniments are simple yet effective and should be within the range of most pianists.

Breath marks are given throughout, showing the most musically desirable places to take a breath.

ANY DREAM WILL DO

(from "Joseph and the Amazing Technicolor® Dreamcoat")

Music by Andrew Lloyd Webber. Lyrics by Tim Rice

Take care with the dotted rhythms. Keep the semiquavers light and try to match the accompaniment.

THE SKATER'S WALTZ

By Emil Waldteufel

Try to play the last eight bars in a single breath.

EENSY, WEENSY SPIDER

American traditional

You'll need to snatch a quick breath in bar 16. Don't be late on the second beat!

Quite lively

PAVANE

(from "The Capriol Suite")

By Peter Warlock

Try for a smooth, sustained sound, but be sure to tongue each note quite firmly.

Very steady

I'M POPEYE THE SAILOR MAN

Words & Music by Sammy Lerner

This piece needs a bright and breezy performance!

E D E L W E I S S

(from "The Sound of Music")

Words by Oscar Hammerstein II. Music by Richard Rodgers

Play each phrase as smoothly as possible. Listen carefully to the tuning.

Moderately

O NO, JOHN!

English traditional

Play the last four bars quite forcefully, for contrast.

SARABANDE

(from "Keyboard Suite IX")

By George Frideric Handel

In this piece it's probably best to breathe every two bars.

I HAVE A DREAM

Words & Music by Benny Andersson & Björn Ulvaeus

Make sure you always take a full breath, even though most of the phrases are short.

THE YELLOW ROSE OF TEXAS

American traditional

Play with a full sound, and make sure you tongue each note.

Quite lively

JEAN DE FLORETTE (THEME)

By Jean-Claude Petit

Take your breaths quickly, so that you don't have to cut the dotted minims too short.

NO MATTER WHAT

Music by Andrew Lloyd Webber. Words by Jim Steinman

Take care with the start of each phrase. It's very easy to be late!

HEY HEY ARE YOU READY TO PLAY

(Tweenies Theme)

Music by Graham Pike & Liz Kitchen. Words by Will Brenton & Ian Lauchlan

Listen hard to the tuning of the octave leaps. Keep the rhythm relaxed.

Steady swing

GUANTANAMERA

Music adaptation by Pete Seeger & Julian Orbon. Words adapted by Julian Orbon from a poem by José Marti

Keep the rhythm very steady. When a phrase ends with a quaver, play the quaver lightly.

BARBIE GIRL

Words & Music by Soren Rasted, Claus Norreen, Rene Dif,
Lene Nystrom, Johnny Pederson & Karsten Delgado

Take a good breath on the first beat of bar 6, to carry you through to the end of the phrase.

THE PHANTOM OF THE OPERA

(from "The Phantom of the Opera")

Music by Andrew Lloyd Webber. Lyrics by Charles Hart. Additional Lyrics by Richard Stilgoe & Mike Batt.

Be absolutely precise with the dotted crotchet/quaver rhythms.

LAND OF HOPE AND GLORY

By Edward Elgar

Try for a very smooth, sustained sound. Don't let the tempo drag.

ALL MY LOVING

Words & Music by John Lennon & Paul McCartney

Be careful to read the rhythms carefully – don't guess!

SOMETHIN' STUPID

Words & Music by C. Carson Parks

Articulate the repeated quavers neatly and evenly.

OOM PAH PAH

(from "Oliver")

Words & Music by Lionel Bart

This piece needs a strong performance, but the middle section should be softer and smoother for contrast.

DANCE TO YOUR DADDY

English traditional

Accent the first beat of each bar slightly, but play the other notes quite lightly.